DORA the EXPLORER

PHONICS
READING PROGRAM

Book 10

D1047817

Click It, Quick!

by Quinlan B. Lee

SCHOLASTIC INC.

New York   Toronto   London   Auckland   Sydney
Mexico City   New Delhi   Hong Kong   Buenos Aires

Señor Tucán is having
an animal picture contest.
He will give us clues.
Then we have to click it,
quick, to win.
Will you help us?
Let's go!

The first clue says:
"Find a bird that likes
to quack.
If you are by the water,
you are on the right track."
Do you see a bird
that likes to quack?

Yes!
A duck lives by the water
and likes to quack.
Let's take his picture.
Click it, quick!

The next clue says:
"This animal lives in
a den that is warm
and snug.
His pointy quills
make him hard to hug."
Do you see an animal
with quills?

Yeah!
It is a porcupine.
Look at his quills.
Let's be quiet
so we don't wake him.
Click it, quick.

The last clue says:
"Find an animal who is quiet and quick.
Swiping things is his favorite trick."
Do you know who it is?
Is it a cat or a mouse or a fox?

It is a fox—Swiper the fox!
Oh, no!
That quick fox wants to
swipe our camera.
Say, "Swiper, no swiping!"
Great! Now we can click
it, quick.

We did it!